Measurement and Geometry

by Marcia Miller and Martin Lee

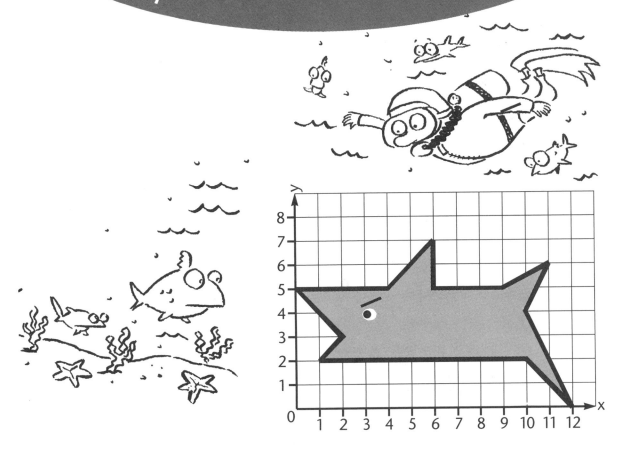

SCHOLASTIC
PROFESSIONAL BOOKS

New York ✳ Toronto ✳ London ✳ Auckland ✳ Sydney

To Highmount

Edited by Sarah Glasscock

Cover design by Jaime Lucero

Interior design by Ellen Matlach Hassell
for Boultinghouse & Boultinghouse, Inc.

Interior illustrations by Michael Moran and Manuel Rivera

ISBN 0-590-37370-6

Contents

(continued on the next page)

✳ Activity includes a student reproducible.

MEASUREMENT

✷ Activity includes a student reproducible.

Introduction

With this book of activities, part of a six-book mathematics series, we hope to make teaching and understanding geometry and measurement fun, creative, and exciting.

⟳ An Overview of the Book

Table of Contents

The table of contents features the activity names and page numbers, as well as stars to mark student reproducibles. Activities are categorized by geometry or measurement topic, so you may use the table of contents as a scope and sequence.

Teaching Pages

Everything you need to know is on the teaching page, but you also have the option of tailoring the activities to meet the students' individual needs and to address the wide variety of skills displayed in your classroom.

Learning Logo

A logo indicating the geometry or measurement topic being discussed appears at the top of the page. The logo is correlated to the topics in the table of contents. This will enable you to key the activities to your mathematics curriculum quickly and easily.

Learning Objective

The objective clearly states the primary aim of the activity.

Grouping

This states whether the whole class, individual students, pairs, or cooperative groups should perform the task. If an activity lends itself to more than one grouping, the choices are indicated. Again, if you feel that another grouping is more appropriate to your classroom, feel free to alter the activity accordingly.

Materials

To cut your preparation time, all materials necessary for the main activity (including student reproducible) and its extension are listed. Most of the materials are probably already in your classroom. If an activity has a student reproducible with it, the page number of the reproducible is listed here.

Advance Preparation

A few activities require some minimal advance preparation on your part. All the directions you need are given here. You may also let students take over some or all of the preparation.

Directions

The directions usually begin with suggestions on how to introduce or review the geometry or measurement topic, including any terms and/or formulas.

Step-by-step details on how to do the activity follow. When pertinent, specific strategies that might help students in solving problems are suggested.

Taking It Farther

This section on the teaching page offers suggestions on how you can extend and enrich the activity. Students who require extra help and those who need a challenge will both benefit when you move the activity to a different level.

Assessing Skills

The key questions and/or common errors pointed out in this section will help alert you to students' progress. (In fact, you may want to jot down more questions on the page.) Use the information you gather about students here in conjunction with the teacher assessment form that appears on page 63 of the book.

Answers

When answers are called for, they appear at the bottom of the teaching page. If the answer is in the form of a drawing or diagram, it appears on page 64, and you're advised of that at the bottom of the teaching page.

Student Reproducibles

About one-third of the activities have a companion student reproducible page for you to duplicate and distribute. These activities are marked with a star in the table of contents.

Do I Have Problems!

These pages are filled with fun and challenging Problems of the Day that you may write on the board or post on the bulletin board. The answers appear in brackets at the end of each problem.

Assessment

Student Self-Evaluation Form

At the end of the activity, hand out these forms for students to complete. Emphasize that their responses are for themselves as well as you. Evaluating their own performances will help students clarify their thinking and understand more about their reasoning.

Teacher Assessment Form and Scoring Rubric

The sign of a student's success with an activity is more than a correct answer. As the NCTM stresses, problem solving, communication, reasoning, and connections are equally important in the mathematical process. How a student arrives at the answer—the strategies she or he uses or discards, for instance—can be as important as the answer itself. This assessment form and scoring rubric will help you determine the full range of students' mastery of skills.

National Council of Teachers of Mathematics Standards

The activities in this book, and the rest of the series, have been written with the National Council of Teachers of Mathematics (NCTM) Standards in mind. The first four standards—Mathematics as Problem Solving, Mathematics as Communication, Mathematics as Reasoning, and Mathematical Connections—form the philosophical underpinning of the activities.

Standard 1: Mathematics as Problem Solving
The open-ended structure of the activities, and their extension, builds and strengthens students' problem-solving skills.

Standard 2: Mathematics as Communication
Class discussion at the beginning and ending of the activities is an integral part of these activities.

Additionally, communication is fostered when students work in pairs or cooperative groups and when individuals share and compare work.

Standard 3: Mathematics as Reasoning
Communicating their processes in working these activities gives students the opportunity to understand and appreciate their own thinking.

Standard 4: Mathematical Connections
A variety of situations has been incorporated into the activities to give students a broad base on which to apply mathematics. Topics range from real-life experiences (historical and contemporary) to the whimsical and fantastic, so students can expand their mathematical thinking to include other subject areas.

More specifically, the activities in this book address the following NCTM Standards.

NCTM Standards Grades K–4:

Standard 9: Geometry and Spatial Sense
* Describe, model, draw, and classify shapes.
* Investigate and predict the results of combining, subdividing, and changing shapes.
* Develop spatial sense.
* Relate geometric ideas to number and measurement ideas.
* Recognize and appreciate geometry in their world.

Standard 10: Measurement
* Understand the attributes of length, capacity, weight, mass, area, volume, time, temperature, and angle.
* Develop the process of measuring and concepts related to units of measurement.
* Make and use estimates of measurement.
* Make and use measurements in problems and everyday situations.

NCTM Standards Grades 5–8:

Standard 12: Geometry
* Identify, describe, compare, and classify geometric figures.
* Visualize and represent geometric figures with special attention to developing spatial sense.
* Explore transformations of geometric figures.
* Represent and solve problems using geometric models.
* Develop an appreciation of geometry as a means of describing the physical world.

Standard 13: Measurement
* Extend students' understanding of the process of measurement.
* Estimate, make, and use measurements to describe and compare phenomena.
* Select appropriate units and tools to measure to the degree of accuracy required in a particular situation.
* Understand the structure and use of systems of measurement.
* Extend their understanding of the concepts of perimeter, area, volume, angle measure, capacity, and weight and mass.
* Develop the concepts of rates and other derived and indirect measurements.
* Develop formulas and procedures for determining measure to solve problems.

Inside Out

It's easy to tell whether your canary is outside or inside its cage. It's not always so easy to tell whether a point is outside or inside a geometric figure.

⟳→ Directions

1. Duplicate and distribute the *Inside Out* reproducible.

2. Review with students what a simple closed figure is. Draw examples like the ones below on the board or overhead projector for discussion. Ask volunteers to describe what they see.

Simple Open Figures	Simple Closed Figures
□ ⌀ < ◎	△ ○ D ⌐ ▭

3. Present this plan to help students determine whether a point is outside or inside the figure. Invite discussion and clarification of the steps as necessary.

   a. Plot a new point well outside the figure.

   b. Using a straightedge, connect the outside point with the point in question.

   c. Count all intersections of the line segment and the figure. Repeat with other points and other figures. Ask: *What conclusions can you draw?* [An odd number of intersections means a point is inside the figure; an even number of intersections means it's outside.]

4. Have students complete the reproducible and verbalize their discoveries.

☆ Taking It Farther

Let students create new Inside Out figures for classmates to analyze. Some students might explore whether the Inside Out rule applies to complex figures.

✓ Assessing Skills

✹ Do students adequately test initial conclusions to see that they always work?

✹ What generalizations do students make?

✹ Can they apply their generalizations to new figures?

LEARNING OBJECTIVE

Students determine whether a point lies outside or inside a simple closed figure.

GROUPING

Individual or pairs

MATERIALS

✹ overhead projector (optional)

For each student or pair:
✹ *Inside Out* reproducible (p. 9)
✹ straightedge

ANSWERS

A. inside
B. outside
C. outside
D. inside

Inside Out

Where is the point in each figure—inside or outside? Use the intersection method. Record your findings in the table.

A

B
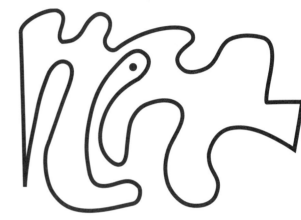

C
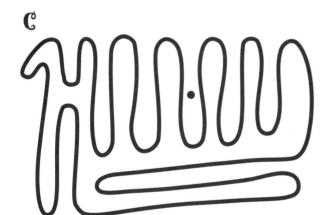

D

FIGURE	INTERSECTIONS	INSIDE?	OUTSIDE?
A			
B			
C			
D			

What's the Angle?

Just about everybody likes a good puzzle. To solve the one in this activity, students use what they know about angle measures.

◌➔ Directions

1. Duplicate and distribute a copy of the *What's the Angle?* reproducible to each student.

2. Review the concept of angle measurement and the use of a protractor. If necessary, review the meaning of *ray, endpoint, vertex,* and *angle.*

3. Draw a horizontal ray on the board or overhead projector. Label its endpoint *V*. Ask a volunteer to turn the ray into angle *V*, which measures 90°.

4. Have students complete the reproducible on their own. If necessary, demonstrate how to crack the code by doing one example with the class.

5. After students complete the page, you may wish to tell them that Jorge Ojeda-Guzman's tightrope was 36 feet long. He positioned it 35 feet above the ground. As curious spectators gathered, he would walk, dance, or balance himself on a chair.

✭ Taking It Farther

Challenge students to create angle riddles for classmates to solve. Or have them use protractors to measure the angles formed by classroom objects, such as a stapler, open book, closet door, and so on.

✔ Assessing Skills

✳ Do students complete each angle from the endpoint of the given ray?

✳ Do they use protractors correctly to draw the specified angles?

✳ Can students use visual estimation to predict which letter each new ray will (or will not) pass through?

LEARNING OBJECTIVE

Students use protractors and straightedge to complete angles of certain measure to decode an answer.

GROUPING

Individual

MATERIALS

✳ overhead projector (optional)

For each student:
✳ *What's the Angle?* reproducible (p. 11)
✳ protractor
✳ straightedge

ANSWERS

TIGHTROPE

What's the Angle?

Jorge Ojeda-Guzman of Orlando, Florida, holds a world record. He spent 205 straight days—from January 1 to July 25, 1993—on a piece of equipment. On what did he set his unusual endurance record?

**The answer is in code at the bottom on the page.
To crack it, follow these steps:**

1. From the endpoint of each given ray, draw an angle to the specified measure. Use a protractor for accuracy.

2. The angle will intersect a number. Find this number in the code. Write the vertex letter above it.

3. Draw all the angles to find the answer.

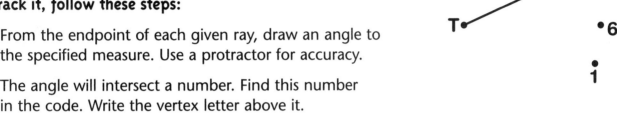

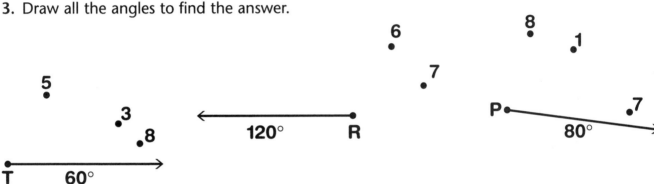

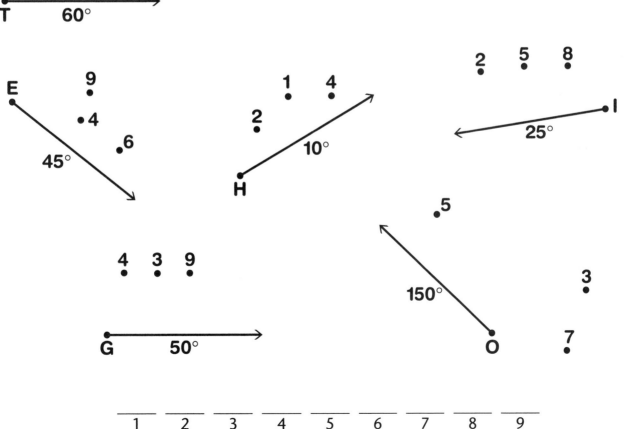

____ ____ ____ ____ ____ ____ ____ ____ ____
  1   2   3   4   5   6   7   8   9

Musical Math

Musicians and monotones alike can practice mathematical communication by investigating the properties of instruments.

Directions

1. Obtain one or more triangles (the percussion instrument) from your school's music department or from a set of basic rhythm instruments. Show the triangle to students. You might have a volunteer play it for the class.

2. Challenge students to describe the triangle using as many mathematical terms as they can. For instance, they can give its geometric name, find the measures of its angles, the lengths of its sides, its perimeter, the area it encloses, its weight, the diameter of the tubing used to form it, the length of the striker, and so on.

3. Have students work in pairs or cooperative groups to describe, measure, analyze, sketch, and label drawings of the triangle or other musical instruments. Encourage them to discover as many mathematical ways to describe the instruments as they can. Make a variety of measuring tools available, such as tape measures, scales, calipers, stopwatches, and so on.

4. Students may present their analyses in any way they wish. Their presentations should be concise, precise, and easy for someone else to follow.

Taking It Farther

Help students explore the physics of music by analyzing an instrument in terms of its fundamental frequencies and overtones, pitch range, range of volume, average length of the decay of a tone, and so on. Guide them in describing, measuring, and presenting this information to add to their analyses.

Assessing Skills

* Do students find a wide variety of ways to describe their instruments?
* How accurately and clearly do they present their findings?

LEARNING OBJECTIVE

Students use mathematical terms to describe, analyze, quantify, and evaluate various musical instruments.

GROUPING

Pairs or cooperative groups

MATERIALS

* various musical instruments
* assorted measuring tools (tape measures, scales, calipers, stopwatches)
* drawing paper
* markers

Eye Spy

Visual/spatial problem solving is a key part of mathematical thinking. What strategies do students apply to solve "shapes-in-a-shape" puzzles?

⟳→ Directions

1. Draw a 3 × 3 grid on the board or overhead projector. Discuss with the class how to identify all the squares in the figure. [14] Some students will say that they see nine squares, which is only the number of its 1 × 1 squares. Guide them to see that the figure also contains 2 × 2 and 3 × 3 squares.

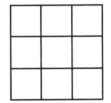

2. Model how to make an organized list to count all sizes of squares. You can use colored chalk or a marker to trace or shade different size squares to help students better visualize them.

3. Draw 4 × 4 and 5 × 5 squares. Have students find the number of squares in each. [30; 55] Then guide them in identifying a pattern to find the total number of squares in any size square grid.
   [**Pattern:**
   3 × 3 square—number of 1 × 1 squares, 9; number of 2 × 2 squares, 4; number of 3 × 3 squares, 1; 9 + 4 + 1 = 14
   4 × 4 square—number of 1 × 1 squares, 16; number of 2 × 2 squares, 9; number of 3 × 3 squares, 4; number of 4 × 4 squares, 1; 16 + 9 + 4 + 1 = 30
   5 × 5 square—number of 1 × 1 squares, 25; number of 2 × 2 squares, 16; number of 3 × 3 squares, 9; number of 4 × 4 squares, 4; number of 5 × 5 squares, 1; 25 + 16 + 9 + 4 + 1 = 55]

☆ Taking It Farther

Present similar problems using triangles-within-triangles.

✓ Assessing Skills

* Can students visualize squares of different sizes in a figure?
* What techniques do students use to identify and count the squares?
* Do they record their information in an organized way?

LEARNING OBJECTIVE

Students develop and apply strategies to identify and count all the squares in a figure.

GROUPING

Individuals or pairs

MATERIALS

* colored chalk, markers, or pencils
* overhead projector (optional)

Tangram Investigations

Tangrams, the Chinese puzzles, are centuries old. Students examine the geometric relationships among the seven pieces as they create their own sets.

➤ Directions

1. Duplicate and distribute a set of the *Tangram Investigations* reproducibles to each student.

2. As needed, help students work through the steps for making the pieces of the set. Guide them in looking at the diagrams carefully.

3. Encourage students to experiment with their tangram pieces to form other, different figures. Challenge them to form letters of the alphabet, numerals, animals, people, tools, vehicles, and so on.

4. Display students' creations. Or have them trace around the outside of each completed figure to form a template other students can fill in.

★ Taking It Farther

Ask students to fill in some of the tangram templates classmates have made. You can also let students combine sets of tangrams to make larger figures.

✔ Assessing Skills

✳ Do students follow the directions to create the seven tangram pieces?

✳ Can they use the pieces to make the different figures described?

✳ Are students able to create more complicated figures?

LEARNING OBJECTIVE

Students make a set of tangrams and form several shapes and representations of different objects.

GROUPING

Individuals, pairs, or whole class

MATERIALS

Fore each student:

✳ *Tangram Investigations* reproducibles (pp. 15, 16)

✳ square sheet of paper (6 to 8 inches on a side)

✳ scissors

✳ markers

ANSWERS

See page 64.

Tangram Investigations

You've seen a tangram—the seven-piece geometric puzzle. Here, you'll create a set of tangram pieces and then use them to form shapes and figures.

Start with a square sheet of paper. Follow the steps below and the diagrams to create your set of tangram pieces.

1. Fold your paper in half along the diagonal.
Cut along the fold.
Fold each triangle in half.
Then cut along the fold of one of these triangles.
Label the two small triangles.
These are your first two tangram pieces.

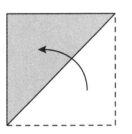 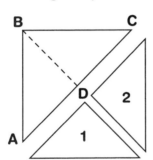

2. Fold the large triangle so that B meets D.
Cut along fold EF.
Label this triangle.
It's your third tangram piece.

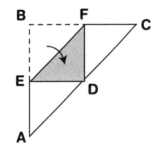 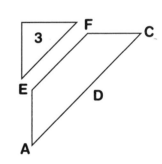

3. Fold C so that it meets D.
Draw line GD parallel to FH.
Cut along GD and FH.
Label the triangle and the square.
They're the fourth and fifth pieces.

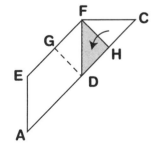 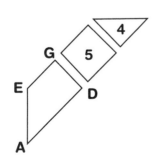

4. Fold D to meet E.
Cut along the fold.
Label the triangle and the parallelogram—your last two tangram pieces.

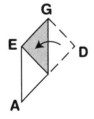 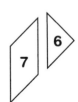

5. Now make a square with your seven tangram pieces.

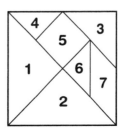

Tangram Investigations

Now that you've got your tangram set, you can use the pieces to make a variety of shapes and figures. Use all seven pieces each time. Draw a diagram to show how you made the following:

1. a right triangle	**2.** a rectangle that is not a square
3. a parallelogram that is neither a square nor a rectangle	**4.** a trapezoid
5. a candle	**6.** a boat
7. an animal of any kind (Try a cat, dog, fish, or bird.)	**8.** a figure of your choice

Geometry Concentration

Here's an old tried-and-true game revised to help students reinforce their knowledge of geometric terms, drawings, and symbols.

⟳→ Directions

1. With the class, brainstorm a list of at least 20 geometric figures and terms that students can represent with a simple drawing. List these terms on the board. Examples include *line segment, point, ray, right angle, obtuse angle, straight angle, scalene triangle, isosceles triangle, quadrilateral, trapezoid, rhombus, hexagonal pyramid, hypotenuse, diameter, cone, sector, perpendicular lines, interior angle,* and so on.

2. Divide the class into cooperative groups. Have each group make a set of geometry cards. Each set needs one pair of cards for each of 20 (or more) geometric terms. One card names the term, such as parallel lines; the matching card shows a simple drawing of parallel lines. Be sure students understand that one card has words only, and its match has drawings only.

3. After the cards are prepared, a student in each group shuffles them well. Then someone deals them out, facedown, in rows and columns on a table or playing area. Students use the rules of Concentration. To play, one player turns over any two cards. If the cards match (that is, if they show a geometric term and its illustration), that player keeps the cards and takes another turn. If the cards don't match, the player replaces them facedown where they were, and the next player goes. Play continues in turn until all cards are matched.

☆ Taking It Farther

Make alternate decks that include other geometric terms and symbols. Or apply the idea of this game to other areas of math, such as measurement, number facts, or decimals, fractions, and percents.

✔ Assessing Skills

✳ Observe as students play the game. How readily do they recognize pairs of related cards?

✳ Is it more difficult for students to recognize matches or to recall where cards are?

LEARNING OBJECTIVE

Students identify and match geometric drawings, symbols, and terms.

GROUPING

Cooperative groups

MATERIALS

For each group:
✳ 40 index cards
✳ rulers

Bulletin Board Logic

Want to stimulate students' creativity, humor, and inductive reasoning skills? Then set up this interactive bulletin board.

➤ Directions

1. Set aside bulletin board space for this activity. Give it a title, such as "What's My Rule?" or "Property Room."

2. Display a set of figures that go together because they share geometric attributes. Also give some counterexamples to help students isolate the common attribute(s) in the first set. Give each set a silly name, for example:

These are blorguls.	These are not blorguls.
⌐ 〈 ⌒⌒	◇ ∞ ⌐

3. Help students identify the attributes blorguls share. Discuss why the figures in the second group are not blorguls. [Blorguls are closed figures with a curve and a right angle.]

4. Each day, post a new set of examples, counterexamples, and "unknowns," all on index cards or self-stick notes. Invite students to discover the rule and then sort the "unknowns" into the correct sets. You might provide a blank space in which students write the rule in their own words.

5. Encourage students to add other examples to the display. Have them tell how they form generalizations and apply their reasoning to test unknowns.

★ Taking It Farther

Provide examples only, without counterexamples. Ask students to draw other figures that fit the rule. Or have students create their own examples and counterexamples for classmates to analyze.

✓ Assessing Skills

✴ How do students form their generalizations?

✴ Do their original examples always observe the rule?

LEARNING OBJECTIVE

Students use logical reasoning to make generalizations about geometric properties and apply their generalizations to new situations.

GROUPING

Whole class

MATERIALS

✴ index cards or self-stick notes

Models in Space

Students handle solid figures to sharpen their ability to visualize geometry in three dimensions.

⟿ Directions

1. Display assorted materials. Students pick the materials they want to use to construct space figures. Or present different materials on different occasions to provide a variety of construction experiences.

2. Have individual students or pairs make six different space figures. For example, they can tightly roll and tape sheets of newspaper into long tubes, which they can cut to desired lengths and tape together at the ends to form cubes, pyramids, or prisms. They can also make these figures with straws and clay or toothpicks and marshmallows. They can use construction paper or oak tag to form cylinders or cones.

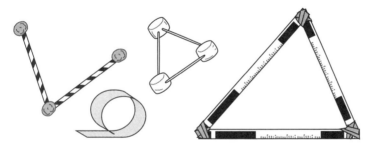

3. Allow time for students to display their models and refer to them to answer questions such as: *How many faces in a pyramid? How many vertices in a hexagonal prism? How many edges in a cone?* Students can make tables to list the number of faces, edges, and vertices for each type of figure. Ask them to describe similarities and differences among the solid shapes.

☆ Taking It Farther

Let students experiment with their space figures to determine which is the strongest, the weakest, or the most versatile as a building module.

✓ Assessing Skills

✳ How many different space figures do students make?

✳ What generalizations can they make about space figures?

LEARNING OBJECTIVE

Students construct models of space figures.

GROUPING

Individual or pairs

MATERIALS

✳ newspaper
✳ straws
✳ modeling clay
✳ mini-marshmallows
✳ toothpicks
✳ construction paper
✳ oak tag
✳ rulers
✳ scissors
✳ tape

Any Way You Slice It

When you slice an apple pie, you know what you expect to see. But when you slice a clay figure, it's not always so clear what you'll find inside.

⟲→ Directions

1. Give each pair or group some modeling clay and a plastic knife or large paper clip they can unbend and use as a cutting wire.

2. First have students mold the clay into solid figures—cones, cubes, spheres, cylinders, prisms, and pyramids.

3. Then ask them to predict the shapes of faces that would be exposed if they cut through the figures at various angles. Tell them first to name and sketch the shape of each face they visualize. Then they should slice the clay to verify their predictions. After each cut, students should draw the actual shape of the exposed face if it differs from their prediction.

4. Along with instructing students to make different cuts in the same figure, you can have them make cuts in the same orientation through different figures.

5. Discuss patterns that emerge. Encourage students to present their findings in tables or drawings.

☆ Taking It Farther

Have students predict how many different polygonal faces they can form by slicing a cube in all possible ways. They can make a cube and slice it to check their predictions.

✔ Assessing Skills

✳ Observe students as they form the solid figures. Check that the figures embody the required properties.

✳ How well do students visualize the shapes of faces before they cut? Does their ability to predict the shapes improve as they work?

LEARNING OBJECTIVE

Students explore the shapes of faces that have been cut into solid figures.

GROUPING

Pairs or cooperative groups

MATERIALS

✳ modeling clay
✳ plastic knives or large paper clips
✳ drawing paper
✳ pencils

Mapping Up

Anyone can build a tower of blocks, but it takes practice in spatial and visual reasoning to create a map that matches the structure.

⟳→ Directions

1. Build the structure shown using 10 cubes, or draw it on the chalkboard or on an overhead projector.

2. Then draw the map shown on the chalkboard or on an overhead projector.

3. Guide students to see that the map and the cube structure contain the same information. Have them verbalize the relationship between the structure and its map. [Each square on the map tells how many cubes rise above it.] You may want to point out that a map like this is called a base drawing.

4. To provide practice at this, have pairs of students use cubes to make some simple towers and then make a map to go with each one.

5. Duplicate and distribute the *Mapping Up* reproducible to each pair. Also give each pair several sheets of grid paper and drawing paper.

2	3	2
1	1	1

☆ Taking It Farther

Invite students to work with partners. One creates an elaborate cube skyscraper that contains several wings and towers of different heights. The other makes a map that matches the structure. Students can exchange roles.

✓ Assessing Skills

✱ Do students see the relationship between each structure and its map?

✱ Can students make a cube structure given its map?

✱ Can they make a map given a picture or model of a structure?

LEARNING OBJECTIVE

Students explore the relationship between a 3-dimensional structure and a 2-dimensional map of it.

GROUPING

Pairs

MATERIALS

✱ *Mapping Up* reproducible (p. 22)

✱ centimeter cubes or snap cubes

✱ grid paper

✱ drawing paper

✱ markers

✱ overhead projector (optional)

Mapping Up

Build or draw a cube structure for each map shown.

1.

2	2	2	2
3	4	4	3
2	2	2	2

2.

2	3	4	
3	4	5	
	5	6	5
		4	3	2
		2	1

3.

7	4	4	3		4	4	4
4	6	4	3		5	5	
3	6		3	4	5		4
3					4			3

Draw a map for each cube structure shown.

4.

5.

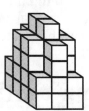

Are You Sure?

Do your students complain that you ask them to do the impossible? Well, with this activity, they may be right!

◉→ Directions

1. Set aside bulletin board space for this activity. Give it a title, such as "Is This Possible?" or "Are You Sure?"

2. Display descriptions of geometric figures with specific attributes, such as a scalene right triangle or a regular pentagon. Include some descriptions of figures that are impossible to draw, such as an equilateral right triangle or a quadrilateral with three right angles.

3. Invite students to draw an example of each figure on an index card or self-stick note, which they post beneath each description. Accept as many different examples of each figure as students can draw. As an alternative to using index cards or self-stick notes, students can draw right on a large sheet of chart paper or butcher paper that has the descriptions written on it.

4. If students think a particular figure is impossible, they can write this on a card with an illustration or explanation of why they think so.

5. Every day or so, post new descriptions. Resolve conflicts among drawings. Take time to discuss with students why they cannot draw the impossible examples.

☆ Taking It Farther

On one side of a bulletin board, post descriptions of geometric figures. On the other side, post, in scrambled order, examples of these figures cut from magazines, catalogs, or newspapers. Challenge students to match each description with its example.

✔ Assessing Skills

✳ How do students determine whether it is possible for them to draw a figure?

✳ Are students able to explain why a figure is impossible to draw?

LEARNING OBJECTIVE

Students use an interactive bulletin board to explore geometric possibilities by trying to draw figures with certain characteristics.

GROUPING

Whole class

MATERIALS

✳ index cards or self-stick notes

✳ thumbtacks

✳ chart paper or butcher paper (optional)

Icosa-Questions

An *icosahedron* is a solid figure with 20 faces. Get students to do some solid problem solving by playing this variation of Twenty Questions.

⟳ Directions

1. Review the game Twenty Questions: Someone is "It." "It." picks an unknown object without telling the group what it is. To identify the object, players take turns asking questions that can be answered only by yes or no. Players may have up to 20 guesses to figure out the answer.

2. Play Icosa-Questions the same way. The player who is "It." picks a plane or solid geometric figure as the unknown object. Suppose It picks an isosceles right triangle. Here's how the questioning might begin:

   Question 1: Is it a space figure? [no]
   Question 2: Is it a polygon? [yes]
   Question 3: Does it have more than four sides? [no]
   Question 4: Does it have four sides? [no]

   By this point, most players will know that the figure is a kind of triangle.

3. Play a demonstration game with the class. Model how to formulate useful questions. Help students interpret answers by asking, "What do you now know for sure?" "What figure can you eliminate now?" or "What would you like to know?"

4. Form cooperative groups. Each group needs someone to be "It." and someone to keep track of the number of questions asked. Everyone else guesses.

5. Remind groups to listen carefully to each other's questions and answers so they can accumulate enough information to identify the geometric object in 20 guesses or fewer. Students should trade tasks in subsequent rounds.

☆ Taking It Farther

Broaden Icosa-Questions to include geometric concepts, such as *parallel, area, perimeter, volume,* and so on. Encourage students to ask an early question to learn whether the unknown object is a figure or a concept.

✓ Assessing Skills

✳ How well do players formulate their questions?

✳ Does "It." answer accurately and objectively?

✳ How do groups collaborate to identify the unknown object?

LEARNING OBJECTIVE

Students play a logic game that involves asking and answering yes and no questions to identify a geometric figure.

GROUPING

Cooperative groups

MATERIALS

None

Figure with Figures

Students use mental math as they play a game about geometric properties.

➤ Directions

1. In a brainstorming session with the class, list geometric properties students can count. For instance:
   * number of faces a rectangular pyramid has (or hexagonal prism, triangular pyramid, cube, and so on)
   * number of angles an octagon contains (or hexagon, decagon, and so on)
   * number of vertices a cube has (or triangular prism, pentagonal pyramid, and so on)
   * number of diagonals a hexagon has (or octagon, heptagon, and so on)
   * number of edges a cylinder has (or cone, cube, and so on)

2. Divide the class into pairs or groups. Have each pair or group prepare a set of 20 to 25 cards, each of which gives one property, such as the number of faces a cube has, from the class list. Pairs or groups should prepare an answer key on a separate sheet of paper to refer to as they play.

3. One student shuffles the cards. In turn, each player draws a card and determines the number of the property described. That number becomes the player's score. If the player gives an incorrect answer, he or she earns no points that round. The first player to accumulate 25 or more points wins. Pairs may take turns keeping score, and groups may designate a scorekeeper.

✪ Taking It Farther

Vary the game by including statements with larger numbers, such as the number of degrees in a right angle, the sum of the interior angles of a triangle, and so on. Change the target score to reflect the new data.

✔ Assessing Skills

* How do students verify whether an answer is right or wrong?
* Which properties are most challenging for students to figure out?

LEARNING OBJECTIVE

Students determine the number of faces, edges, and vertices for geometric figures.

GROUPING

Pairs or cooperative groups

MATERIALS

* 20–25 index cards per group or pair
* markers
* paper

Geometry Jumble

Students can apply their critical-thinking and problem-solving skills to solve a puzzle that combines geometric terms with spelling.

⟶ Directions

1. Duplicate and distribute a copy of the *Geometry Jumble* reproducible to each student or pair.

2. Tell students to unscramble each word, the letters of which they write in the given spaces. When the puzzle is completed, the highlighted letters in each word will spell the answer to the question.

3. You may want to provide a word list students can consult as they work. The words, in alphabetical order, are *angle, cone, perpendicular, point, prism, pyramid, ray, segment, sphere, vertex,* and *volume.*

4. When students finish the puzzle, you may tell them that the original castle at Gomdan, Yemen, had 20 stories and was built sometime prior to A.D. 100. Allow time for students to find Yemen on a world map or globe.

☆ Taking It Farther

Invite students to make up their own Geometry Jumble puzzles for classmates to solve. They can hide a fun fact in the words. Or highlighted letters can, when they are unscrambled, reveal a bonus geometry word.

✓ Assessing Skills

✳ Do students know what each geometry term means? If not, what do they do to find out the meaning?

✳ How do students use the word list, if it is available to them?

LEARNING OBJECTIVE

Students unscramble geometry terms to solve a riddle.

GROUPING

Individual or pairs

MATERIALS

✳ *Geometry Jumble* reproducible (p. 27)

✳ world map or globe

✳ word list (optional)

ANSWERS

1. SEGMENT
2. CONE
3. VOLUME
4. PERPENDICULAR
5. RAY
6. ANGLE
7. PYRAMID
8. SPHERE
9. PRISM
10. VERTEX
11. POINT

GOMDAN, YEMEN

Geometry Jamble

Where is the world's oldest castle found?

To find out, unscramble each geometry word. Write the correctly spelled word in the spaces provided—one letter per space. When you finish, read the highlighted letters from top to bottom for the location.

1. NESTMEG   __ __ ☐ __ __ __ __

2. NECO   __ ☐ __ __

3. ELMOVU   __ __ __ ☐ __ __

4. CRINAPPLERUDE   __ __ __ __ __ ☐ __ __ __ __ __ __ __

5. AYR   __ ☐ __

6. GLEAN   __ ☐ __ __ __

7. YAMDRIP   __ ☐ __ __ __ __ __

8. PESHER   __ __ ☐ __ __ __

9. MIRPS   __ __ __ ☐ __

10. REXVET   __ __ ☐ __ __ __

11. PINTO   __ __ __ ☐ __

Right Angle Tic-Tac-Toe

The plotting will surely thicken as students play this graphing game.

◉→ Directions

1. Have students make a first-quadrant coordinate grid whose axes number from 0 to 10. You may also prepare the grids in advance.

2. Tell students that the object of the game is for a team to plot five adjacent Xs or Os to form a right angle, for example, (2,2), (3,2), (4,2), (4,1), and (4,0).

3. To play, divide the class into groups or pairs. Then divide each group or pair into two teams—Team X and Team O. Team X names the coordinates of a point they want to plot and then plots it. Then Team O names and plots its desired point. Play continues in turn this way.

4. Each team judges the accuracy of the other team's plotting. If a team names a point already taken, or a point off the graph, the turn is lost.

5. Encourage teams to play defensively as well as offensively.

6. The first team to plot five adjacent Xs or Os that form a right angle wins the game.

☆ Taking It Farther

Play using other quadrants of the coordinate grid. Or change the rules so that teams form a seven-point right angle, a square, or another shape they agree on.

✔ Assessing Skills

✳ Do students correctly name and plot points on the coordinate grid?

✳ What strategies do teams use to win or to defend?

LEARNING OBJECTIVE

Students use visual/spatial reasoning and coordinate geometry to play a game in which they try to plot five adjacent points that form a right angle.

GROUPING

Cooperative groups or pairs

MATERIALS

✳ centimeter grid paper

✳ markers

28

Finger Twister

**Students who are "all thumbs" needn't worry.
This game's for the other four fingers!**

◎→ Directions

1. Ask students who know the party game Twister to describe it. Review the rules if needed. This game is like Twister, but the mat is a coordinate grid.

2. Divide the class into groups of 4. Each group needs three things—a coordinate grid labeled from 0 to 5 on each axis, a cardboard spinner in fourths labeled to indicate fingers: I (index), M (middle), R (ring), and P (pinkie), and a number cube or number cards labeled 0 to 5. Help students as needed to make the spinners and coordinate grids. If number cubes are used, instruct students to cover the 6 on the cube with tape and write a zero on the face.

3. Discuss the object of the game—to put the specified finger of one hand only (NO thumbs!) on a point on the grid. Once a finger is placed, it must stay there unless, in a future turn, the spinner calls for the use of that finger again.

4. To play, the first player spins to see which finger to place, then rolls the number cube twice (or picks two number cards) to form an ordered pair. The player places that finger on that point and keeps it there as other players move. A player is out if his or her finger slips off its point, or if the player uses his or her thumb. Play continues in turn until no one can move or until all but one player is out. The last player left "standing" wins. All fingers go on the same grid, so entanglements will arise!

5. If a player can't place the finger on a point because another finger already occupies it, he or she may reverse the order of the number pair to create another point. If that doesn't work, the player may roll (or pick) once more.

☆ Taking It Farther

Have students play with larger coordinate grids. Or they can make a floor mat with a plastic shower curtain and masking tape to play with right and left hands and feet.

✓ Assessing Skills

* Do students accurately locate points on the coordinate grid?
* What tricks do students use to help them hold their positions on the grid?

LEARNING OBJECTIVE

Students play a game to locate points on a coordinate grid.

GROUPING

Cooperative groups of 4

MATERIALS

* inch (or larger) grid paper
* cardboard
* markers
* paper clips and pencils to make spinner divided into fourths
* number cards or number cube labeled 0–5
* correction tape
* masking tape (optional)
* plastic shower curtain (optional)

Rectangle Hunt

Knowing a rectangle's area doesn't mean knowing its dimensions. In this game, students use logic and geometry to find a rectangle on a coordinate grid.

⟳→ Directions

1. Review the definition of rectangle. Remind students that a square is a kind of rectangle.

2. Divide the class into cooperative groups. Each group makes a coordinate grid with axes labeled from 0 to 10 on grid paper.

3. One person "hides" a rectangle on the coordinate grid so that the sides follow grid lines and the corners fall on intersections. That player shields the grid from the others' view and finds the area in square units of the hidden rectangle. Its area is given as the opening hint.

4. The rest of the group then tries to identify the corners of the hidden rectangle. To do so, they take turns naming coordinate pairs. The person who has drawn the rectangle tells whether each named point is outside, inside, or on the rectangle. Players keep track of points named and responses given.

5. Play continues until the group locates the four corners of the rectangle. Their score is the number of guesses it took to find all the corners. Players switch tasks and play again. The lower score wins.

☆ Taking It Farther

Make the game more difficult by not giving the area of the rectangle. Or let players hide a parallelogram or a rhombus.

✔ Assessing Skills

✳ What strategies do students use to keep track of the information they learn with each guess?

✳ How logically do subsequent guesses follow from information learned?

LEARNING OBJECTIVE

Students try to identify the coordinates of a rectangle hidden on a coordinate grid.

GROUPING

Cooperative groups

MATERIALS

✳ grid paper
✳ markers

Shark Stretch

It's knowledge of coordinate geometry and functions, not skill at aquatic aerobics, that's the key to success in this activity.

⟫ Directions

1. Tell students to imagine a rectangle plotted on a grid. Ask them to predict what would happen to the appearance of that rectangle if they doubled its *x* coordinates. [It will be twice as long.] Then ask them to predict what the figure would look like if both its *x* and *y* coordinates were doubled. [It would be a similar shape twice as long and twice as tall.] Discuss students' responses. Invite them to sketch rectangles on grid paper to test their guesses. Alternatively, you might show the changes on an overhead projector or with a computer graphing program or graphing calculator.

2. Duplicate and distribute a copy of the *Shark Stretch* reproducible to individuals or pairs.

3. Circulate and observe students as they plot and analyze their drawings. Guide them to list each new set of ordered pairs. When students finish, have them compare their findings and generalizations.

☆ Taking It Farther

Challenge students to design and plot their own animals or objects and compare how changing the coordinates in each ordered pair in the same way affects the figures' shapes and areas. Ask them to determine how the changes affect the perimeters of the figures.

✓ Assessing Skills

✳ What do students notice about the functional relationships among the shark drawings?

✳ What generalizations can they make based on the drawings they've plotted?

LEARNING OBJECTIVE

Students explore how changing *x* and *y* values of ordered pairs affects the appearance of a figure on a coordinate grid.

GROUPING

Individual or pairs

MATERIALS

✳ *Shark Stretch* reproducible (p. 32)

✳ straightedge

✳ colored pencils

✳ grid paper

✳ overhead projector (optional)

✳ computer graphing program or graphing calculator (optional)

ANSWERS

See page 64 for grid drawing.

1. about 32 square units

2. The shape is elongated; it's twice as long and the same height as the original.

3. about 64 square units, twice that of the original

4. The shark is squashed; it's twice as high but the same length as the original; area is about 64 square units, twice that of the original.

5. The figure has the same shape as the original.

6. about 128 square units, four times its original size

Shark Stretch

Grab your pencil and straightedge. You're going to change the shape of a shark without relying on brute strength—just a little "coordination."

On the grid, plot and connect in order the following points:

(12, 0), (10, 4), (11, 6), (9, 5),

(6, 5), (6, 7), (4, 5), (0, 5),

(2, 3), (1, 2), (10, 2), (12, 0).

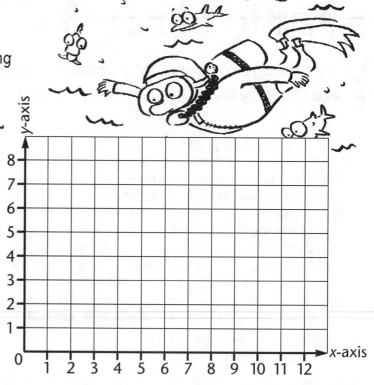

1. What is the area of your shark? _____

Draw another grid. Double each *x* value in the first grid and plot the new shark.

2. In what ways is it like the original shark? How is it different?

_____

_____

3. What is the area of the new shark? _____

Draw another grid. Double each *y* value in the first grid and plot this new shark.

4. How is this shark like the original? How is it different? What is its area?

_____

_____

Draw yet another grid. Double each *x* and *y* value from the first grid and plot this new shark.

5. What do you discover?

_____

_____

6. What is this shark's area? _____

Art Explosion

Before machines made easy enlargements and reductions possible, artists applied proportional thinking and visual reasoning to make copies of different sizes.

⟲➤ Directions

1. Display a transparency grid. Invite a volunteer to draw a simple geometric figure on it.

2. Display a transparency grid of another size. Discuss with students how to "copy" the drawing onto the second grid, where it will be either larger or smaller. Guide students to examine the figure box by box and copy what they see on one grid into the analogous boxes on the other. This procedure will produce a pair of similar drawings.

3. Now have students make their own copies. Provide assorted line drawings or cartoons from which they can pick. Or let them select their own drawings or cartoons to copy. Provide two sizes of grid paper. If necessary, model how to superimpose a grid onto the drawing to facilitate the copying process (refer to item 2).

4. Display the originals with students' copies. Talk about the process with the class. Encourage students to share their strategies and impressions.

★ Taking It Farther

Try a similar activity using maps, photographs, works of art, or product logos. Encourage students to make both an enlarged and a "shrunken" version of the same picture to compare and contrast the process.

✔ Assessing Skills

✳ What organizational techniques do students employ in this process?

✳ How accurately does the copy reflect the original?

LEARNING OBJECTIVE

Students apply the concepts of ratio, proportion, and similarity to make similar drawings.

GROUPING

Individual

MATERIALS

✳ overhead projector

✳ transparency grids in two sizes (for example, inch and half inch)

✳ line drawings or cartoons

✳ grid paper in several sizes

Partner Symmetry

Double students' creativity by having partners form symmetrical designs.

⟲→ Directions

1. Divide the class into pairs. Hand out the manipulatives with which they can form designs. Choose from the materials listed, or use whatever is at hand.

2. Give each person a piece of yarn or string to use as a line of symmetry, which can be placed horizontally or vertically on the work area of the grid or dot paper. Each person makes a design on only one side of the line. Encourage students to create complex and inventive designs. Designs should also be 3-dimensional.

3. At a signal, partners switch seats. Each person now tries to complete the other person's design by creating the symmetrical missing half on the other side of the line of symmetry.

4. Partners then return to their original designs to see whether their partner's design forms an exact symmetrical duplicate.

5. Discuss the process with the class. Invite students to describe any difficulties they encountered.

☆ Taking It Farther

Try the same activity, but have pairs use grid or dot paper and colored markers or crayons. Or students may prepare half of a drawing on plain paper around a line of symmetry, to be completed by a partner.

✓ Assessing Skills

✳ Are the completed designs symmetrical?

✳ Are students more adept at beginning or at completing a design?

LEARNING OBJECTIVE

Students apply concepts of symmetry to complete a 3-dimensional figure around a given line of symmetry.

GROUPING

Pairs

MATERIALS

✳ pattern blocks, color tiles, snap cubes, or Cuisenaire rods

✳ yarn or string

✳ grid paper or dot paper

✳ colored markers or crayons

✳ drawing paper

Pentominetris

Students play a low-tech variation of the computer game Tetris.

✦ Directions

1. Duplicate and distribute a copy of the *Pentominetris* reproducible to each student. Identify the 12 figures as a set of pentominoes, each formed by five centimeter cubes joined in different ways.

2. Provide students with envelopes, colored markers or crayons, and scissors. Have each one prepare two sets of pentominoes for the game. Students shade or color each pentomino and then carefully cut them it and place it in the envelope.

3. Form game groups. Each group needs a piece of centimeter grid paper as a game board and the prepared sets of pentominoes. Players in a group may combine all their pentominoes into one envelope.

4. To play, each player in turn randomly draws a pentomino from the envelope and puts it, colored side up, anywhere on the grid. All outer edges of the pentomino must align with grid lines. A player may slide or turn a pentomino into any orientation to fit the available space. Pentominoes may interlock but may not overlap or extend beyond the borders of the grid. Pentominoes may not be flipped to the unshaded side.

5. If a pentomino can't fit anywhere on the grid, the player who picked it is out. The last player who can place a piece wins.

☆ Taking It Farther

Vary the rules to allow students to pick once more before they're out. Or use a smaller portion of the centimeter grid paper, such as an 8 by 12 area, for a more challenging game.

✔ Assessing Skills

✳ Observe how students place the pentominoes. What strategies do they use?

✳ How well do students visualize the pieces in different orientations?

LEARNING OBJECTIVE

Students explore transformational geometry in a game that involves recognizing and manipulating pentominoes.

GROUPING

Cooperative groups

MATERIALS

✳ *Pentominetris* reproducible (p. 36)
✳ envelopes
✳ colored markers or crayons
✳ scissors
✳ centimeter grid paper

Pentominetris

Here are two sets of 12 different pentominoes. Color and cut them out to play Pentominetris. Use a piece of centimeter grid paper as your game board.

Creative Compass Constructions

A compass and colored pencils become powerful tools that students can use to explore geometric patterns involving circles, points, radii, and arcs.

◗ Directions

1. Duplicate and distribute a copy of the *Creative Compass Constructions* reproducible to each student. Also give each student a compass, colored pencils, several sheets of white paper, and have an eraser.

2. Tell students that all figures on the reproducible were created from combinations of arcs and circles only. Have them use a compass to replicate the circle designs they see on the page.

3. Then instruct students to create their own circle and arc designs. Display all completed designs on a geometry bulletin board.

4. Challenge students to replicate each other's original designs.

⭐ Taking It Farther

Ask students to design a class, team, or school logo based on circles and arcs.

✔ Assessing Skills

✳ How do students go about trying to replicate a given design?

✳ What observations do students make about arcs, circles, radii, and points?

LEARNING OBJECTIVE

Students use compasses and colored pencils to create interesting designs.

GROUPING

Individual

MATERIALS

✳ *Creative Compass Constructions* reproducible (p. 38)

✳ compass

✳ unlined white paper

✳ colored pencils

✳ erasers

Creative Compass Constructions

Each of these designs was made with a compass and a pencil . . . and sometimes an eraser. Can you figure out how to reconstruct them?

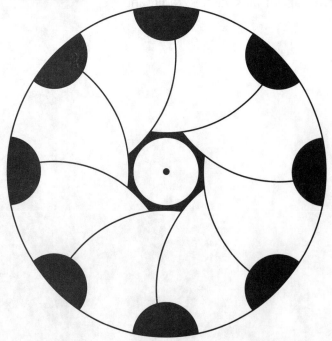

Measurement Scavenger Hunt

Students can sharpen their skills in estimating and visual/spatial reasoning by holding a classroom scavenger hunt.

➔ Directions

1. Prepare a checklist of items students must find in the classroom. Describe each item in terms of some kind of measurement—metric, customary, or both. Include length, width, height, weight, perimeter, area, and volume. Here are some examples:
   * a book that weighs between 500 and 750 grams
   * a pencil less than 5 inches long
   * a student taller than 175 centimeters
   * a picture whose perimeter is about 20 inches
   * a container whose volume is about 36 cubic inches
   * a circle whose diameter is 8 to 10 centimeters
   * a coin whose circumference is about 7 centimeters

2. Discuss the scavenger hunt rules with students. For instance, do they collect each item, or is it enough for them to identify and describe it? Who verifies measurements, and when? What time limit, if any, should be set?

3. Conduct the scavenger hunt according to the rules you establish. Give each individual hunter or pairs or groups of hunters a checklist of items and access to measurement tools.

4. After the hunt is completed, allow time for students to share how they found, estimated, and measured one item.

☆ Taking It Farther

Have students try a similar activity at home with family members. They can use the same checklist or make up their own. Or have students make up their own checklist of items for an outdoor measurement scavenger hunt.

✔ Assessing Skills

* Observe as students work on the measurement scavenger hunt. What estimation skills or benchmarks do they employ?
* Do students' estimation skills improve as they work?
* With which kinds of measuring skills do students need more practice?

LEARNING OBJECTIVE

Students locate classroom objects of given length, weight, volume, area, or perimeter.

GROUPING

Individual, pairs, or cooperative groups

MATERIALS

* scavenger hunt checklist (see left)
* assorted measuring tools

Measuring Across and Down

What's the abbreviation for pound? What 7-letter word means ten decades?

◉▸Directions

1. Duplicate and distribute a set of the *Measuring Across and Down* reproducibles to each student or pair. Page 41 has the puzzle grid and page 42 provides the clues.

2. If necessary, review how to solve a crossword puzzle. Remind students that each word they use in the puzzle grid must fit its clue exactly.

3. Have students work on the puzzle independently or in pairs. Allow them to consult a dictionary for correct spelling or refer to their math books to verify clues.

☆ Taking It Farther

Challenge students to create their own crossword puzzles using units of metric measure, geometry terms, or other categories of math words.

✔ Assessing Skills

✸ How do students figure out the answers to the clues?

✸ What do students do when they're stuck?

LEARNING OBJECTIVE

Students review and reinforce relationships and definitions of customary units of measure by solving a crossword puzzle.

GROUPING

Individual or pairs

MATERIALS

✶ *Measuring Across and Down* reproducibles (pp. 41–42)

✶ dictionary (optional)

ANSWERS

Across	Down
3. MONTHS	1. CARAT
6. GALLONS	2. HOUR
9. MILLENNIUM	4. OZ
11. PINTS	5. HALF GALLON
15. DECADES	7. INCH
16. MINUTE	8. CUP
18. ACRES	9. MILES
20. CUP	10. MIDNIGHT
21. YEAR	12. TEN
22. FT	13. QUART
23. TON	14. HALF
24. SECONDS	15. DEGREES
27. CENTURY	17. POUNDS
29. DAYS	19. OUNCE
30. BUSHEL	21. YARDS
31. WEEKS	25. ONE
	26. SIX
	28. LB

Measuring Across and Down

All the clues in this puzzle are about units of customary measure. Along with
the puzzle grid, you'll also need the clues, which are on the next page.

Measuring Across and Down

ACROSS

3. A year has 12 _____.

6. These contain four quarts.

9. one thousand years

11. A quart equals two _____.

15. groups of ten years

16. $\frac{1}{60}$ of an hour

18. One hundred sixty of these equal one square mile.

20. $\frac{1}{4}$ of a quart

21. 52 weeks

22. abbreviation for the unit that has 12 inches

23. A small car might weigh about 1 _____.

24. A minute has sixty of these.

27. one hundred years

29. A fortnight has 14 _____.

30. This unit of measure equals 4 pecks or 32 dry quarts.

31. A non-leap-year February has exactly four of them.

DOWN

1. unit of weight for gems and precious stones

2. $\frac{1}{24}$ of a day

4. abbreviation for the unit that is $\frac{1}{8}$ of a cup

5. Four pints is one of these.

7. $\frac{1}{36}$ of a yard

8. eight fluid ounces

9. 10,560 feet = 2 _____

10. another way to say 12:00 A.M.

12. years in a decade

13. $\frac{1}{4}$ of a gallon

14. Twenty-six weeks is this part of a year.

15. units for measuring temperature

17. A typical cat might weigh 10 _____.

19. $\frac{1}{128}$ of a gallon

21. A mile has 1,760 _____.

25. 3,600 seconds = _____ hour

26. half a dozen

28. abbreviation for weight equivalent to 16 ounces

Hidden Meters

It's easy to recognize a meter on a meterstick. But what if a meter is broken into different units and scattered on a puzzle?

⟳ Directions

1. Review the relationships among metric prefixes as well as how to convert from one metric unit to another.

2. Duplicate and distribute a copy of the *Hidden Meters* reproducible to each student. Tell them that the grid has 16 trios of measurements that combine to make 1 meter. The hidden meters can be found by identifying three measures in a row vertically, horizontally, or diagonally whose sum is 1 meter; for example, 40 cm + 2 dm + 400 mm = 1 m. Students ring the sets of three boxes. Some rings overlap.

3. You may let students use calculators. Alert them to enter numbers with the decimal point in the correct position in order for the calculator to be useful.

☆ Taking It Farther

Make up similar game grids in which you vary the units to present measurement sums of 1 gram or 1 liter.

✓ Assessing Skills

What techniques do students use to make conversions among units?

ANSWERS

90 mm	11 cm	0.8 m	500 mm	40 cm	25 cm	0.5 m	0.25 m
200 mm	50 dm	60 cm	1 dm	30 cm	9 mm	1 cm	0.8 m
40 cm	1 cm	700 mm	8 cm	5 cm	4 dm	550 mm	50 cm
400 mm	0.3 m	300 mm	3 dm	40 cm	0.3 m	0.4 m	300 cm
2 dm	3 dm	40 mm	15 mm	1.1 m	300 mm	9 m	0.5 m
0.3 cm	1 m	30 cm	600 mm	1 dm	8 dm	20 cm	350 mm
50 cm	0.45 m	1 dm	45 cm	2.5 cm	0.1 m	9 dm	15 cm
200 mm	3 dm	50 cm	0.95 m	4 cm	3 cm	0.80 m	40 dm
10 mm	250 mm	600 cm	4.5 cm	0.07 m	600 mm	70 cm	300 mm

Hidden Meters

Find three boxes horizontally, vertically, or diagonally whose sum is 1 meter.
There are 16 such trios. Ring each trio you see. You may use a calculator.

90 mm	11 cm	0.8 m	500 mm	40 cm	25 cm	0.5 m	0.25 m
200 mm	50 dm	60 cm	1 dm	30 cm	9 mm	1 cm	0.8 m
40 cm	1 cm	700 mm	8 cm	5 cm	4 dm	550 mm	50 cm
400 mm	0.3 m	300 mm	3 dm	40 cm	0.3 m	0.4 cm	300 cm
2 dm	3 dm	40 mm	15 mm	1.1 m	300 mm	9 m	0.5 m
0.3 cm	1 m	30 cm	600 mm	1 dm	8 dm	20 cm	350 mm
50 cm	0.45 m	1 dm	45 cm	2.5 cm	0.1 m	9 dm	15 cm
200 mm	3 dm	50 cm	0.95 m	4 cm	3 cm	0.80 m	40 dm
10 mm	250 mm	600 dm	4.5 dm	0.07 m	600 mm	70 cm	300 mm

Measurement and Geometry Scholastic Professional Books

Lengthy Words

At times, students may think that words carry little weight. But this activity will prove that words carry length!

◉→ Directions

1. Duplicate and distribute a copy of the *Lengthy Words* reproducible to each student or pair.

2. Review measuring to the nearest half centimeter (5 millimeters).

3. Present this code for the alphabet letters: A = 0.5 cm, B = 1.0 cm, C = 1.5 cm, D = 2.0 cm, and so on, through Z = 13.0 cm. Tell students that if a line segment measures 5.5 cm, for instance, then its letter value would be K.

4. For a group of line segments, students measure to find the letter value for each segment. Then they arrange those letters into one or more words.

5. You may want to do one example with the class. Then have students complete the activity on their own or in pairs.

✪ Taking It Farther

Encourage students to make their own sets of segments for classmates to measure and decode. Or, challenge students to try the reverse: to draw a set of segments to represent given words.

✔ Assessing Skills

✳ Do students measure accurately?

✳ How well do students form words from the letters they find? Can they find more than one word for a given set of letters?

LEARNING OBJECTIVE

Students measure line segments to the nearest half centimeter, assign letter values to the lengths, and use the measurements to form words.

GROUPING

Individual or pairs

MATERIALS

✳ *Lengthy Words* reproducible (p. 46)

✳ centimeter ruler

ANSWERS

Segments measure in cm.

1. 2.0, 2.5, 7.0, 10.0 (DENT/TEND)

2. 2.5, 1.5, 4.0, 7.5 (ECHO)

3. 3.0, 6.0, 0.5, 7.5 (FOAL/LOAF)

4. 10.0, 4.5, 6.5, 2.5, 9.0 (TIMER/REMIT/MITER)

5. 1, 10.5, 3.5, 3.5, 12.5 (BUGGY)

6. 1.5, 0.5, 5.5, 2.5 (CAKE)

7. 5.0, 0.5, 11.5 (JAW)

45

Lengthy Words

Measure the segments in each open figure. Determine the letter
values, based on the code A = 0.5 cm, B = 1.0 cm, C = 1.5 cm, and
so on. Make as many words as you can from each set of letters.

1.

5.

2.
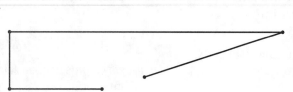

3.

4.
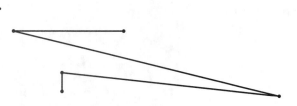

6.

7.
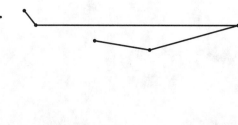

Pin That Area

Geoboards or dot paper and the trusty old alphabet can provide new ways for students to explore perimeter and area.

⟳→ Directions

1. Tell students that it is possible to use one or two rubber bands on a geoboard to form every uppercase letter of the alphabet. Some letters require a little imagination to create, but each is possible, some in several ways.

2. Have students predict a range of areas and perimeters for the letters. For example, they might guess that E has a greater perimeter than V or that the area of Q is greater than the area of I. Suggest that they sort their predictions into two lists: least/middle/greatest perimeter; least/middle/greatest area.

3. Provide geoboards and rubber bands or dot paper to pairs or groups. Students form block letters on the geoboards or dot paper and then calculate their perimeters to the nearest linear unit and their areas to the nearest square unit.

4. When students finish, instruct them to compare their estimates with the measured areas and perimeters they found. Encourage groups to share and compare their discoveries.

☆ Taking It Farther

Encourage students to perform a similar activity with the numerals 0 to 9.

✓ Assessing Skills

✳ Can students form every letter of the alphabet?

✳ What methods do they use to calculate the perimeters? the areas?

✳ How closely do predictions match measured dimensions?

LEARNING OBJECTIVE

Students form block letters on geoboards or dot paper to explore area and perimeter.

GROUPING

Pairs or cooperative groups

MATERIALS

✳ geoboards and rubber bands or dot paper

✳ colored pencils

Area Irregulars

**Students don't have to cry over spilled milk.
They can figure out how to measure it instead!**

⟲→Directions

1. Draw this figure on the chalkboard or overhead projector. Ask students for suggestions on how to determine the area it encloses. Discuss their ideas.

2. Distribute grid paper. Ask students to draw an irregular shape, similar to the one you've shown, on their grids. Guide them to understand that the area of the shape is the total of all the full and partial squares it encloses.

3. Then present the following method for approximating the area:

   a. Count all squares that lie completely within the outline.

   b. Count all squares through which the outline passes; these lie only partially within the outline. Divide this number by 2.

   c. Add the sum from **a** and **b**. This gives a reasonable estimate of the area of the irregular figure.

4. Have students use this method to estimate the area of the figure they drew on their grid paper. Then have them try it again, using another shape.

5. Duplicate and distribute a copy of the *Area Irregulars* reproducible to individuals or pairs. Allow time for students to compare answers.

☆ Taking It Farther

Challenge students to describe methods for getting an even closer approximation of the area within an irregular figure. Invite them to demonstrate their methods for improving accuracy. [Sample answers: Use smaller squares; subdivide all the squares into fourths, even sixteenths.]

✔ Assessing Skills

✳ Do students understand the method presented for approximating the area of an irregular figure? Can they apply this method correctly?

✳ Can students come up with ways to improve the estimates? Can they explain their methods in a comprehensible way?

LEARNING OBJECTIVE

Students estimate the area of irregular figures.

GROUPING

Individual or pairs

MATERIALS

✳ *Area Irregulars* reproducible (p. 49)

✳ grid paper (ideally, 4 squares/inch)

✳ overhead projector (optional)

ANSWERS

Answers may vary slightly.
Possible answers:

1. 86 square units
2. 53.5 square units
3. 54 square units
4. 58.5 square units

Area Irregulars

Estimate the area enclosed by each outline.

1.

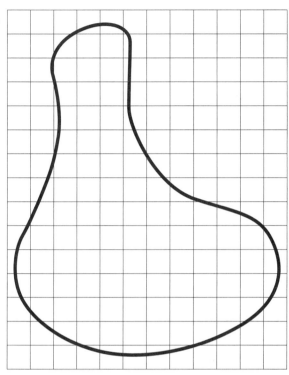

2.

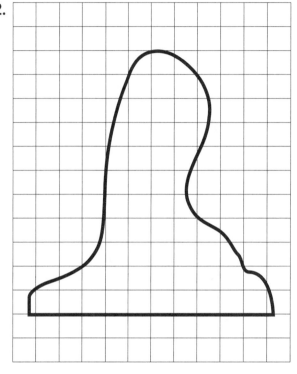

3.

4.

Have a Ball!

Here's an investigation of volume that should keep students bouncing!

⟶ Directions

1. Have students describe the "ball rooms" at children's play facilities. A ball room is a contained area—a room or fenced-off part of a room—full of colorful plastic balls, in which young children roll and romp.

2. Divide the class into cooperative groups. Challenge each group to estimate how many balls it would take to create a children's ball room for playing.

3. Guide groups to determine a reasonable size for the ball room. It must be big enough for many children to play in safely. Encourage students to use proportional reasoning to break down the task to make it manageable. Have grid paper and markers available if students want to make floor plans of their rooms.

4. Ask groups to repeat the investigation for three different sizes of balls. Provide an assortment of balls.

5. When groups finish, have them share their estimates and strategies.

☆ Taking It Farther

Tell students to estimate the cost to fill the play space they plan. Or they can contact a local play facility that has a ball room to find out its dimensions and how many balls it takes to fill the space.

✓ Assessing Skills

* Observe groups during this investigation to see that all members participate actively.

* How do students approach the question, and what strategies do they use?

* Do their estimates make sense?

LEARNING OBJECTIVE

Students estimate and calculate the volumes of rooms and spheres; they apply proportional reasoning and geometric formulas for volume.

GROUPING

Cooperative groups

MATERIALS

* spherical balls of different sizes, such as tennis balls, soccer balls, table tennis balls, softballs, marbles, squash balls, beach balls, and so on

* grid paper and markers (optional)

Gourmet Pet Problems

There's no getting around it: using proportional reasoning can speak volumes for smart shoppers.

✎ Directions

1. Ask students to figure out which is the better buy: a 14-in.-diameter pizza that costs $12, or an 8-in. pizza that costs $6. Challenge them to use mental math.

2. Have students explain their answers and methods. Discuss that the 14-in. pie is the better buy, since it's more than 3 times as large as the 8-in. pie but costs only twice as much. You can ask a volunteer to demonstrate how to use the area formula for circles to show that the larger pie has an area, in square inches, of 153.86 and the smaller one has an area of 50.24.

3. As needed, review the formulas for finding area and volume.
   Area of a circle: $A = \pi \times r^2$
   Volume of a cylinder: $V = \pi \times r^2 \times h$

4. Discuss the concept of unit pricing, and that when comparing two items, the one with the lower unit price is the better buy.

5. Duplicate and distribute the *Gourmet Pet Problems* reproducible to each student or pair. Guide students to use the computation method that makes the most sense—paper and pencil, calculator, or mental math—to solve the problems on the page.

★ Taking It Farther

Ask students to formulate "geometric better buy" problems of their own for classmates to solve. Challenge them, for example, to create pizza problems in which one pie is a circle and the other is a rectangle, or packaged food problems in which one container is a can and the other is a box.

✔ Assessing Skills

✳ Do students apply the correct formulas and use proportional reasoning to solve the better buy problems?

✳ Do they use a computation method that makes good sense?

Gourmet Pet Problems

Imagine that you're shopping for pet food. For each item, you need to choose between similar products. Unfortunately, the labels don't contain unit prices.

Use your knowledge of finding area and volume and of proportions to choose the better buy. Use the computation method that makes sense.

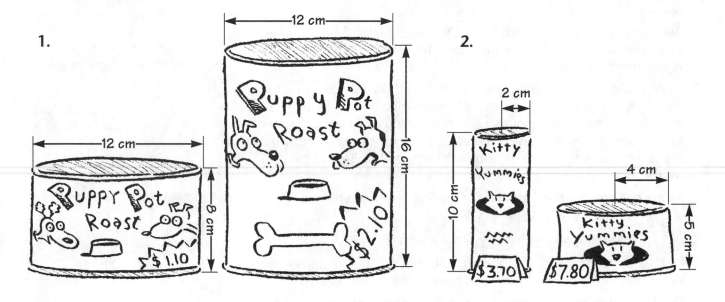

1.

2.

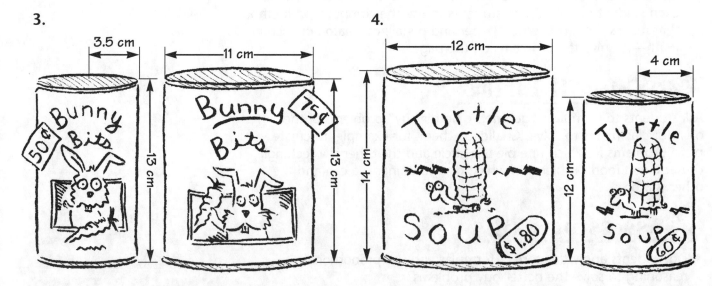

3.

4.

5. Doggie scrapple-and-bone pizzas come in three sizes and two shapes. There are two round pies: a 6-in. one that costs $2.50 and an 18-in. one that costs $12. There's a 12-in. × 19-in. rectangular pie for $6. Which pizza is the best buy?

Design a Wall Unit

Furniture designers use geometry and measurement to create wall units that are functional and attractive. Students try their hand at this creative task.

⟩→ Directions

1. If possible, obtain some furniture catalogs that show different kinds of wall units. Some are open. Others have doors and closed compartments that hold video and stereo equipment. Some have book or display shelves, CD and tape storage areas, drawers, and pull-out desk surfaces.

2. Divide the class into design groups. Challenge each group to design a wall unit for the classroom. Discuss some of the features designers always keep in mind, such as height, width, and depth of available space, adequate storage area for the kinds of things the unit will hold, air circulation space around electronic equipment, interesting and practical design, thickness of wood, and so on.

3. Have groups make labeled scale drawings on grid paper of their wall units. Drawings should include all dimensions and measurements so that someone could use the drawing to build the wall unit.

4. Hold a design showcase where groups can share their designs and explain the unique features. You may also want to conduct a group critique of designs and let all the groups collaborate on an ideal wall unit that includes the best features of all the plans.

✪ Taking It Farther

Invite students to design their ideal room. They can design an area of any shape with an area of 600 square feet of floor space. Have them include any kind of furniture, windows, built-ins, or other features.

✔ Assessing Skills

✳ How thoroughly do students undertake the task?

✳ Do drawings include sufficient details to serve as a preliminary plan?

✳ What observations do students make about each other's plans?

LEARNING OBJECTIVE

Students measure, estimate, and draw to scale wall units to fit a space in their homes.

GROUPING

Cooperative groups

MATERIALS

✳ measuring tools

✳ grid paper

✳ furniture catalogs (optional)

Geometry Jeopardy

Students expect to answer questions in school. In this activity, however, students do the asking.

⟲→ Directions

1. Have a volunteer explain the idea behind the TV game show *Jeopardy.* (Players ask questions which match given answers.) Point out that in Geometry Jeopardy, all questions are in the category of Geometry and Measurement. Students will formulate a question to fit data in the space that player lands on. For instance, if a space says 18 square feet, a good question might be: *What's the area of a rectangle 6 feet long and 3 feet wide?*

2. Give each player a marker, such as a colored cube or counter. Players flip a coin to determine moves: heads = 2 spaces forward, tails = 1 space forward.

3. Divide the class into groups of from 3 to 5. Duplicate and distribute a copy of the *Geometry Jeopardy* reproducible to each group.

4. In each group, one person acts as judge, the others as players. The judge decides if a question is correct. If not, that player moves back 1 space and awaits his or her next turn. If the question is acceptable, the next player goes. The first player to reach the END wins.

5. Before groups play, formulate other rules they may need, such as: If two players land on the same space, can the second person give the same question the first person gave? What happens if the judge makes an error?

☆ Taking It Farther

Have groups create a new board with other answers. Or they can create a game that more closely resembles the television game show, with answers in order of difficulty in geometry and measurement subcategories, such as 2-dimensional shapes, 3-dimensional figures, metric measures, and so on.

✔ Assessing Skills

✳ What strategies do students use to formulate their questions?

✳ How does the judge evaluate the questions?

LEARNING OBJECTIVE

Applying their knowledge of geometry and measurement concepts, students work backward to form questions that fit given answers.

GROUPING

Cooperative groups

MATERIALS

✳ *Geometry Jeopardy* reproducible (p. 55)

✳ centimeter cubes or counters

✳ coins

✳ calculator (optional)

Geometry Jeopardy

The category for all questions is Geometry and Measurement. Each player needs a play marker. Use this game board and a coin to determine moves: heads = move 2 spaces; tails = move 1 space. Ask a question that fits the answer in the space you land on. The judge decides whether to accept your answer. The first player to reach END wins.

Here's an example: The answer is **12 mm**. What's the question?
How about: **What's the radius of a circle whose diameter is 24 mm?**

START

36 square feet

10 cubic inches

30 centimeters

about **78.5** square inches

60 cubic feet

12 square yards

14 miles

90 square meters

12 cubic inches

9 square yards

216 meters

about **56.5** square feet

27 cubic centimeters

1 square foot

26 yards

7.5 square feet

6 cubic yards

120 cubic inches

about **28** square miles

600 square centimeters

END

Analog Angles

Digital clocks may be accurate and easy to read, but analog clocks display lots of geometric possibilities.

➤ Directions

1. Display an analog clock. Point out the angles of different measures that form as the hands move around the clockface.

2. Use a protractor to find the angle measure of the current time.

3. Post these angle questions on the board, overhead projector, or a worksheet. Challenge students to determine an answer for each one.
   * morning times in three different hours when the hands form obtuse angles
   * afternoon times in three different hours when the hands form straight angles
   * a mealtime when the hands form a right angle
   * times in three different hours when the hands form angles of less than 15°
   * times in three different hours when the hands form angles of about 150°
   * three times during the school day when the hands form a right angle
   * the earliest time in your typical day when the hands form a 60° angle
   * an afternoon time when the hands form a 135° angle
   * the latest time in your typical day when the hands form an 11° angle
   * the angle the hands form when your favorite TV show starts

4. To facilitate solving the problems, students can use a real or play clock with movable hands. They can also make or draw clocks as they work.

★ Taking It Farther

Ask students to write riddles about times and angle measures; for instance, "What right angle time sounds like consecutive multiples of the hour?" [5:10]

✓ Assessing Skills

* Observe students as they solve the problems. In what ways do they use analog clockfaces?

* How do students verify their answers?

LEARNING OBJECTIVE

Students visualize angles formed by the hands of an analog clock to solve problems.

GROUPING

Individual or pairs

MATERIALS

* analog clocks
* protractors
* real or play clocks with movable hands
* overhead projector (optional)

Cuckoo Clocks

In this activity, the clock becomes a puzzle that takes visual and spatial reasoning to unravel.

⟲➜ Directions

1. Duplicate and distribute the *Cuckoo Clocks* reproducible to each individual or pair.

2. Tell students that the clock puzzles require visual/spatial reasoning and geometric thinking to solve.

3. Do one demonstration problem from each kind of clock puzzle. Then have students complete the page on their own or in pairs. You may want to have a mirror available for students to use for questions 1–6.

✪ Taking It Farther

Inspire students to create other puzzles like the ones on the reproducible to share with classmates.

✔ Assessing Skills

✳ What strategies do students use to solve the problems?

✳ Which type of puzzles were more challenging to them? Can they explain why?

LEARNING OBJECTIVE

Students use visual/spatial and geometric reasoning to solve puzzles based on analog and digital clockfaces.

GROUPING

Individual or pairs

MATERIALS

✳ *Cuckoo Clocks* reproducible (p. 58)

✳ mirror (optional)

ANSWERS

1. 9:35
2. 8:10
3. 1:50
4. 3:40
5. 6:55
6. 4:20
7. 8:01 or 9:01
8. 11:22, 11:23, 11:32, or 11:33
9. 2:45, 2:46, 3:45, or 3:46
10. 3:00 or 9:00

Cuckoo Clocks

Here are mirror images of analog clocks without numbers. What time is it?

1. _____

2. _____

3. _____

4. _____

5. _____

6. _____

These digital clocks have part of their numerals blocked. What time is it?

7.

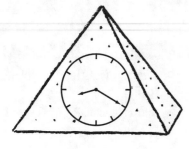

8.

9.

10.

Warmth War

Which is warmer, 35°F or 15°C? If students can figure this out, they have all it takes to win a round of Warmth War.

⟿ Directions

1. Review the formulas commonly used to convert temperatures between Fahrenheit and Celsius.

   Fahrenheit to Celsius: $\frac{5}{9}F - 32 = C$

   Celsius to Fahrenheit: $\frac{9}{5}C + 32 = F$

2. Also review the traditional card game War, in which opponents try to capture cards by turning over a card with a greater value.

3. Divide the class into pairs. Give each pair 40 index cards. One student makes 20 cards with temperatures between 0° and 100° Celsius. The partner makes 20 cards with temperatures between 32° and 212° Fahrenheit. Encourage pairs to prepare cards with a wide range of temperatures.

4. When all cards are ready, students mix them together, then divide the deck into equal piles—one for each player. To play, opponents turn over their top cards. The player whose card gives a warmer temperature wins both cards. If both cards give Fahrenheit or Celsius temperatures, the comparison will be easy. If temperatures are given in different scales, players use estimation or conversion formulas to determine which card is the winner.

5. In case of "war," in which both cards give the same temperature, players use the rules of the traditional game: turn over three more cards. Players compare only the third cards; the winner gets all cards used in that turn.

6. Play continues until one player has captured all the cards.

☆ Taking It Farther

Prepare decks in advance so that the given temperatures fall within a closer range, requiring more frequent use of conversion formulas.

✔ Assessing Skills

✳ Can students use estimation skills to determine the winner of some rounds?

✳ Do students apply the correct formula to convert temperatures?

LEARNING OBJECTIVE

Students use estimation or conversion formulas to compare temperatures given in degrees Celsius and in degrees Fahrenheit.

GROUPING

Pairs

MATERIALS

For each pair:

✳ 40 index cards

✳ markers

✳ calculators

Do I Have Problems!

Here are a variety of geometry and measurement problems to pose to students. Use them as homework puzzles, extra-credit brain teasers, or post them on a Problem of the Day bulletin board.

A DAY'S DAZE
The day before yesterday was Monday, September 30. What day and date will it be the day after the day after tomorrow? [Saturday, October 5]

WHICH WAY IS UP?
Make a Möbius strip from a strip of paper approximately 16 inches long and 1 inch wide. Give it one twist and tape the ends together. Which is the top? Which is the bottom? What's going on here?! [There is no top or bottom; the twist makes it a one-sided strip!]

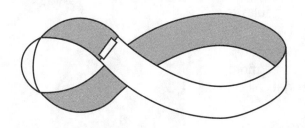

A TRAVEL CLOCK
A clock has a diameter of 17 inches. Its minute hand is 8 inches long. About how far does the point of that minute hand travel over 24 hours? [1,205.76 inches, or about 100.48 feet]

THE 1,000,000TH SECOND
Suppose you want to celebrate the one millionth second of the year. That's a great idea, but when will you celebrate? How can you figure it out? [January 12, 13 hours 46 minutes and 40 seconds into the day, or a little bit after 1:46 P.M.]

GAME'S OVER
The Boston Red Sox are playing the Seattle Mariners on Monday night in Seattle. Larry watches the game on television in Boston. The game starts at 7:40 P.M. Seattle time and lasts for 3 hours and 10 minutes. Larry shuts off the TV as soon as the game ends. When does Larry turn off his TV in Boston? [1:50 A.M. Tuesday]

PIECE OF CAKE
Janet bakes a round cake. She wants to cut it into 11 pieces, but she doesn't care if they are different sizes. She figures out how to do this with only 4 straight cuts. What does she do?

Answer:

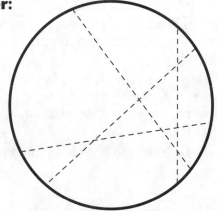

WHAT'S THE POINT?

Avery wrote a paragraph about his classroom, but he left out all the decimal points. Add a decimal point to each measurement so that the statements make sense.

My classroom is big. The ceiling is about 571 m high, and the room is about 148937 cm long. My chair is a good fit for me—it's about 6500 cm high. Out the window I can see train tracks across a field, about 9875 m away.

[5.71 m; 1,489.37 cm; 65.00 cm; 98.75 m]

10 TOOTHPICKS

Use ten toothpicks. Form two squares.

Answer: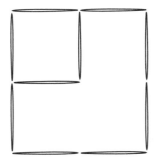

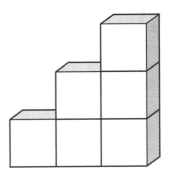

STEP UP

Maris builds a block staircase with 3 steps. How many blocks does she need to build a block staircase with 20 steps? [210 blocks]

WHAT TIME IS IT?

Picture the smallest 4-digit time you'd see on a digital clock. How much later will the greatest 3-digit time appear? [11 hours 59 minutes, from 10:00 to 9:59]

SQUARES EVERYWHERE

Find the total number of squares on a standard chessboard. [204]

SETTING YOUR SITES

The map shows where Maya artifacts were found. Four archaeologists who study the area want to divide the site so each person can examine the same number of artifacts. Draw two straight lines to show how they can do this.

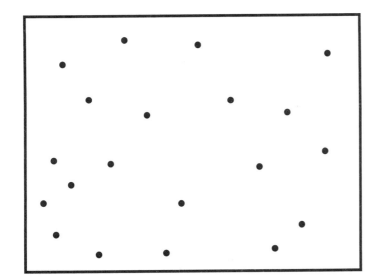

Answer:

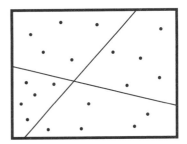

 Name _____ Date _____

In My Opinion

The activity _____ was:

Easy   Hard

because:

_____

_____

_____

My work on this activity was:

poor   fair   good   excellent

because:

_____

_____

_____

I used the following math strategy or strategies:

⟳→ _____   ⟳→ _____

⟳→ _____   ⟳→ _____

⟳→ _____   ⟳→ _____

I would share this tip with someone who is about to do this activity:

_____

_____

Student

UNDERSTANDING
- Identifies the problem or task.
- Understands the math concept.

SOLVING
- Develops and carries out a plan.
- Uses strategies, models, and tools effectively.

DECIDING
- Is able to convey reasoning behind decision making.
- Understands why approach did or didn't work.

LEARNING
- Comments on solution.
- Connects solution to other math or real-world applications.
- Makes general rule about solution or extends it to a more complicated problem.

COMMUNICATING
- Understands and uses mathematical language effectively.

COLLABORATING
- Participates by sharing ideas with partner or group members.
- Listens to partner or other group members.

ACCOMPLISHING
- Shows progress in problem solving.
- Undertakes difficult tasks and perseveres in solving them.
- Is confident of mathematical abilities.

SCORING RUBRIC

3	2	1
Fully accomplishes the task.	Partially accomplishes the task.	Does not accomplish the task.
Shows full understanding of key mathematical idea(s).	Shows partial understanding of key mathematical idea(s).	Shows little or no grasp of key mathematical idea(s).
Communicates thinking clearly using oral explanation or written, symbolic, or visual means.	Oral or written explanation partially communicates thinking but is incomplete, misdirected, or not clearly presented.	Recorded work or oral explanation is fragmented and not understandable.

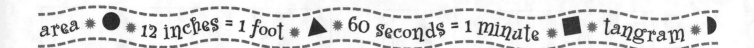
ANSWERS

page 16 Tangram Investigations

1.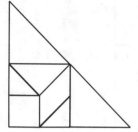

2.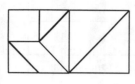

3.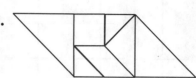

4.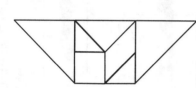

5.

6.

7.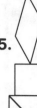

8. Check students' figures.

page 22 Mapping Up

1.

2.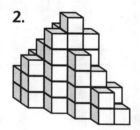

3.

4.
4	4	4
3	4	4
1	2	3

5.
2	4	2
4	5	4
4	5	4
2	4	2

page 32 Shark Stretch

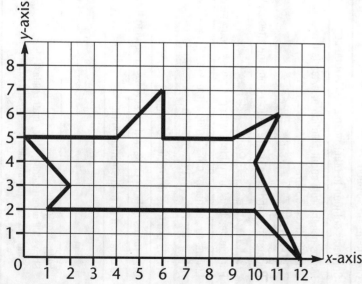